FLAT STANLEY's
WORLDWIDE ADVENTURES

BOOK, No. **11**

Framed in
France

CREATED BY **Jeff Brown**
WRITTEN BY **Josh Greenhut**
PICTURES BY **Macky Pamintuan**

SCHOLASTIC INC.

Text copyright © 2014 by the Trust u/w/o Richard C. Brown a/k/a Jeff Brown f/b/o Duncan Brown. Illustrations by Macky Pamintuan, copyright © 2014 by HarperCollins Publishers. All rights reserved. Published by Scholastic Inc., 557 Broadway, New York, NY 10012, by arrangement with HarperCollins Children's Books, a division of HarperCollins Publishers. SCHOLASTIC and associated logos are trademarks and/or registered trademarks of Scholastic Inc.

12 11 10 9 8 7 6 5 4 3 2 1   14 15 16 17 18 19/0

Printed in the U.S.A.   40

First Scholastic printing, September 2014

Typography by Alison Klapthor

CONTENTS

La Mission Impossible

Stanley Lambchop stood before the map that his teacher, Ms. Merrick, had yanked down at the front of the classroom. She nodded at him to begin.

"I've traveled all over the world," Stanley told his class. "I've been to Canada, Mexico, Egypt, Japan, Kenya, and China." He pointed to each country as he spoke.

His classmate Molly raised her hand. "Do you always travel by mail?" she asked.

Ever since the bulletin board over Stanley's bed had fallen and flattened him, he had been easy to fold and mail in an envelope.

"Not always. Sometimes I fly," Stanley replied. He thought for a moment. "On a plane, I mean. Or I can float thousands of miles if the wind is right."

Stanley's friend Carlos raised his hand next. "So you've never been to Europe?"

Stanley turned and found Europe on the map. He scanned the countries that

made up the continent: England . . . Spain . . . France . . . Germany . . . Italy . . . "Actually, no, I haven't been to *any* of the European countries. . . . But I *have* been to *Australia*." He reached over, past Europe and Asia, and proudly tapped the country in the bottom right corner.

The map shuddered and snapped up like a window shade. All at once it was dark, and Stanley's body felt very tightly wound.

He'd been rolled up with the map!

"Hilph!" Stanley cried. He could hear his classmates laughing.

Suddenly there was a muffled announcement over the loudspeaker.

A moment later
Stanley felt himself
being unwound.

"Stanley," Ms. Merrick
said as she pulled the map
back down. "You are to
report to the principal's office at once."

"But it was an accident!" Stanley
pleaded. "I wasn't trying to be funny.
The map just snapped!"

5

·"I know, Stanley," his teacher said gently. "I'm sure it's nothing serious."

Stanley slouched into the office, but the principal wasn't there. Instead Stanley found someone else—a man he recognized!

"Mr. Dart!" Stanley cried. "What are you doing here?"

Mr. O. Jay Dart was the director of the Famous Museum. Stanley had once helped him catch some art thieves. Stanley had been forced to disguise himself as a shepherd girl in a painting, which was very embarrassing. It was worth it, though, because he caught the thieves red-handed.

"Hello, Stanley," Mr. Dart said, quickly closing the door. "The principal was kind enough to lend me an office. I've come on official business." He laid a leather briefcase on the desk.

"Stanley," he continued as he turned the combination lock on the front of his briefcase. "Have you ever heard of the *Mona Lisa*?"

"The painting?"

"That's right," Mr. Dart said as the case unlocked with a click. "She was painted around 1505 by the great artist and inventor Leonardo da Vinci. When you see her, say hello for me, will you?" Mr. Dart winked mysteriously and lifted the briefcase's lid. A screen rose

from inside with a whirring sound.

Suddenly a dashing man with a polka-dot tie, thick eyebrows, and large, round glasses flickered to life on-screen.

"Stanley, I would like you to meet Agent Lunette of the Police Nationale in Paris, France," Mr. Dart said.

"*Bonjour*, Monsieur Lambchop," the man said in a thick French accent. He looked down his nose. "Eez it true you are v-air-y flat?"

Stanley nodded and turned to the side, and Agent Lunette whistled approvingly.

"Then you are the right boy for the job," Agent Lunette said. "The world's greatest art is going—*poof!*—into thin air, and only you can stop it!" His glasses made his eyes look very large.

Mr. Dart cleared his throat. "There have been a series of art thefts in Paris recently, Stanley," he said. "They believe the *Mona Lisa* will be next."

"Imagine! The *Mona Lisa* stolen from the Musée du Louvre, the greatest art museum in the world!" Agent Lunette cried. "We cannot let this happen!"

"He's right, Stanley," Mr. Dart said. "And as strange as it may seem, you are now a leading expert on museum theft. I've already spoken with your parents, and everything is taken care of. You'll be flying to Paris and staying with your aunt Simone."

Mr. Dart pressed a button, and the on-screen display split in two. "Staaaaaanley!" Stanley's aunt Simone squealed as she appeared on half of the screen beside Agent Lunette. Stanley hadn't seen his aunt since he was small,

but he remembered her bright-red lips and her stylish red hair, which fell in a slant across her face.

"Hi, Aunt Simone!" Stanley said.

"Let me see how you've grown!" she said, gesturing for Stanley to turn around. "*Mon chéri!* You are too thin! You must come to Paris and eat!" she crooned.

"I'm not too thin, Aunt Simone," said Stanley. "I'm flat."

"Come!" Aunt Simone repeated. "We will delight in the City of Light! The food! The fashion! The culture!"

Agent Lunette cleared his throat. "*Pardonnez-moi*, Mademoiselle. But Monsieur Lambchop cannot be seen in public in Paris. His presence will be a secret."

Aunt Simone huffed. "No, *pardonnez-moi*, Monsieur! My nephew will enjoy his visit!"

"No, no!" Agent Lunette snapped. "*Absolument non!* Absolutely not!"

"*Oui!*" Aunt Simone shouted back. "Yes!"

Aunt Simone and Agent Lunette glared at each other from opposite sides of the screen.

"We'll have fun, Aunt Simone, I promise," Stanley interrupted. "And don't worry, Agent Lunette. I'll keep a low profile."

Aunt Simone and Agent Lunette

both nodded grudgingly.

Mr. Dart glanced at his watch. "Your flight leaves in a few hours, Stanley. We'd better get you packed!"

Hello, Please, and Thank You

In an empty airplane hangar, Mr. Dart stood holding a floppy hat with a fur brim and a shirt with puffy sleeves. "While in France, you will be disguised as a member of King Francis I's court, as painted by the magnificent Renaissance painter Jean Clouet," he told Stanley.

Stanley blinked. "You mean I have to change *now*?"

"I'm afraid so," Mr. Dart said, handing Stanley the hat and shirt. "The only way to keep your arrival secret is for you to travel like any other priceless work of art."

Stanley changed his clothes, and a makeup artist powdered his skin and attached a beard on his face. When he was finally ready, Stanley climbed inside the frame. Because it was only a portrait from the waist up, he had to fold his legs behind the canvas.

Mr. Dart stepped back and looked Stanley over. "Clouet painted all the most important people in France during the early sixteenth century," he said. "But if I do say so myself, this may be his best work."

Mr. Dart carefully lifted Stanley's frame and laid it in a wooden crate. The crate had airholes and was filled with shredded paper for comfort. "Your mother has sent a cheese sandwich, some celery sticks, a bag of pretzels, and a juice box for your trip," he said, placing a small bag in Stanley's hand. "Also, here is a French dictionary and a book light. Good luck, Stanley."

"Thank you, Mr. Dart."

Then Mr. Dart closed the crate tightly, and Stanley's adventure began.

It was a little bumpy when Stanley was loaded onto the plane, but then

the crate came to a rest. Soon he heard the roar of the airplane's engines, and everything tilted upward. The plane had taken off.

Stanley switched on the book light and opened the French dictionary. He heard his mother's voice in his head. "The three most important phrases in any language are *hello*, *please*, and *thank you*," she had once told him. "A polite visitor is a welcome one."

Stanley turned to the *H*s and found the word *hello*. He already knew that one: *bonjour*.

Please was harder. Stanley frowned. The French phrase seemed like a strange jumble of letters: *s'il vous plaît*.

Was it "sill vows plate"? But then he read that it was pronounced quite simply: "see voo play." "See voo play," Stanley repeated.

And finally *thank you.* "*Merci,*" Stanley said, stressing the "ee" sound on the end.

"*Bonjour, s'il vous plaît, merci,*" Stanley said over and over, until he became very sleepy.

Stanley awoke with a jolt as the plane touched down on the runway. Before long he heard French voices and was suddenly jostled around as the crate was lifted and carried off the plane. After a few minutes—and a bumpy ride—the crate was set down again.

The top was pried off, and Stanley squinted in a sudden glare of morning light coming in through the window. He was in a bare room at the airport. Staring down at him was an officer in uniform.

"*Bonjour*!" Stanley said brightly.

The officer jumped. "The art, it talks!" He gasped, staggering backward.

Agent Lunette stepped in front of the man.

"*Bonjour*, Monsieur Lambchop," Agent Lunette said. "Please excuse my associate. He has never seen a painting like you before." He shook Stanley's hand.

Aunt Simone muscled Agent Lunette aside. "Stanley!" She bent down and kissed Stanley on one cheek and the other.

"*Bonjour*, Aunt Simone!" said Stanley. "Will you help me out of my frame, *s'il vous plaît*?"

His aunt carefully slid him out of his frame and stood him on solid ground.

"*Merci!*" Stanley said, happy to have used his third French phrase. But all of a sudden his legs felt funny, and he slumped to the floor.

"What is wrong?" Aunt Simone shrieked.

"My legs must have fallen asleep," Stanley said. "I've had them folded behind me for the whole trip. I just need to bend them back and forth for a minute, and then I'll be able to stand up."

Aunt Simone looked horrified. "This is how you welcome your guests?" she said to Agent Lunette as Stanley stretched. "By putting them in a box until they turn to mush?"

"Madame," said Agent Lunette. "We had to transport Monsieur Lambchop in this way to keep his mission a secret."

Aunt Simone wagged her finger. "It is against the Rights of Man! It is a crime!"

"Non!" Agent Lunette protested.

"Oui!" Aunt Simone said.

Stanley sprang up in between his aunt and Agent Lunette. *"S'il vous plaît!"* he said. His legs were awake now. "I'm okay. Really."

They glared at each other over Stanley's head. Then his aunt turned away in a huff.

"The Louvre opens in a few hours," Agent Lunette said, recovering his composure. "We have prepared breakfast for you here, and then we will depart for the museum."

"Merci," Stanley said. "I'm starving!"

"Madame, will you join us?" Agent Lunette said, turning toward Aunt Simone.

Aunt Simone scowled at him then slowly nodded, reluctantly following them into the next room. There was a small table set with a white tablecloth. At each place setting was a plate with several rolls of different shapes and sizes, a boiled egg in a small cup, and a glass of orange juice. In the center was a bowl of fresh fruit, a vase of flowers, and crystal salt and pepper shakers.

After sitting down and putting his napkin on his lap, just as his mother had taught him, Stanley took a rectangular roll and bit into it. It was warm and light and buttery and sweet all at the same time—and in the center was a pocket of gooey chocolate.

Stanley closed his eyes and slumped back against his chair. It was the most marvelous thing he'd ever eaten—except, perhaps, for La Abuela's secret ingredient, which he'd learned how to prepare in Mexico.

"What *is* this?" said Stanley in a daze.

"*Pain au chocolat,*" Aunt Simone said. "Bread with chocolate."

"It's so delicious," cooed Stanley.

Agent Lunette and Aunt Simone exchanged small smiles.

"This is France," Aunt Simone said. "Everything is delicious."

Hanging in the Louvre

After breakfast it was time for Stanley to climb back into his painting. Agent Lunette repacked him in his crate, but at Aunt Simone's insistence, the top of the crate was only gently shut. This meant Stanley was able to raise the lid a tiny bit and peek out as Agent Lunette and the other officer carried him toward the Louvre.

They were walking by a giant modern glass pyramid in the courtyard of a very large, old, important-looking building.

"The Louvre is one of the greatest art museums in the world," Agent Lunette said in a low voice. "More than eight million people from all over the globe visit each year."

They passed by a line of security guards and entered the building.

"The thieves have targeted the finest museums in Paris. Centre Georges Pompidou. Musée d'Orsay. One after the other, their most famous paintings have been stolen in broad daylight, during museum hours."

"But how?" Stanley whispered as they passed a statue of a sphinx the size of a lion. Now they were walking past a series of mummies. Stanley hadn't seen one of those since he'd been to Egypt.

"We do not know," Agent Lunette said. A statue of a woman with wings but no head towered over them. "They were swapped with fakes, without anyone noticing until it was too late."

They walked through hall after hall lined with paintings in gold-colored frames and filled with glowing faces against dark backgrounds.

Finally Agent Lunette and the other officer set the crate down gently. "Because of the thefts, all museums in Paris are closing early. The Louvre will close at three o'clock this afternoon. You will guard the *Mona Lisa* until then."

Agent Lunette carefully lifted

Stanley's frame and peered into his eyes. "You are a spy here, Monsieur Lambchop," he whispered. "Do not give yourself away. Do not smile. Do not sneeze. Do not move a muscle. You are a great painting by a Renaissance master. Act like it."

"Absolument!" said Stanley, pulling himself up straighter as he said his fourth French phrase. Agent Lunette hung him carefully on the wall and stepped back to assess the painting. Then he moved forward and straightened Stanley's frame.

"Très bien," he said. "That means 'very good.'"

He turned to walk away. "If by some

chance you are stolen, do not panic," Agent Lunette murmured. "We will find you eventually."

Stanley's eyes widened. "What?"

Agent Lunette looked at his watch. "The museum opens in three minutes and will remain open until three o'clock. After that, you will be able to stretch your legs before returning to your aunt's for dinner at seven. *Bonne chance,* Monsieur Lambchop." And then he translated: "Good luck." He marched out of the room without another word.

Stanley adjusted his arms and was freezing himself into position when he looked up and saw her. Directly across from him, on the opposite wall of the gallery, was the most famous painting of all: the *Mona Lisa*.

It was much smaller than Stanley had expected—no larger than one of the big art books his parents kept in the living room. But even from here, he could see her face: She had the slightest trace of a smile, as if she knew a secret. Her hands were folded calmly before her.

"Mr. Dart says *bonjour*," Stanley whispered.

Moments later the gallery began filling with people. Stanley quickly made his face a blank. A crowd gathered around the *Mona Lisa*, with many people jostling one another to take a photograph of her. Stanley kept his eyes trained on her smile.

It wasn't easy. Every time someone came close to Stanley's painting, he grew terribly nervous.

A group of Asian tourists talked excitedly about his painting for a long time. They must know I'm a fake! he thought.

A man in dark sunglasses studied Stanley's frame. He's plotting to steal me! thought Stanley.

A little girl pointed right at him. She can see my heart beating! thought Stanley.

But eventually everyone moved on to the next painting. Hundreds of people from all over the world walked by. Some barely glanced at Stanley. Some studied him silently for minutes on end.

Hours passed. Stanley grew tired. *Mona Lisa* continued to smile her mysterious smile.

Then a pair of young men walked up and stood in front of Stanley. One said, "Here's another one! Why is everyone in these paintings so serious?"

"Yeah," said the other. "It's like the *Mona Lisa* is the only one with a sense of humor around this place."

Stanley imagined the *Mona Lisa* bursting into laughter. And in that moment he was overcome by an emotion far worse than nervousness or boredom.

Oh no! he thought. I'm getting the giggles!

He bit the inside of his lip.

A woman with an English accent observed Stanley's painting and dryly told her husband, "This painting is more lifelike than you are."

Stanley's sides ached from holding in laughter.

Then a pair of French girls about his age came up to look at him. They were wearing school uniforms. The one on the right had big blue eyes and shiny dark hair pulled back in a ponytail. She tilted her head, looked at Stanley's face, and murmured something to her friend. They both burst out laughing.

At that moment Stanley couldn't help himself! A loud guffaw escaped his lips!

The girls gasped in shock.

An Artist's Eye

Stanley froze quickly. His face went slack. His eyes focused on *Mona Lisa*'s smile.

The girls stared, their mouths hanging open. One of them imitated the sound of Stanley's momentary burst of laughter. They giggled and whispered to each other.

Suddenly their teacher appeared

behind them. She was a tall spidery woman in a long black dress. She said something quick and stern in French. The girls looked at the floor and mumbled apologetically.

One of the girls went across the gallery to the *Mona Lisa*. The girl with blue eyes stayed where she was, pulled out a sketchbook, peered up at Stanley intently, and started drawing.

Stanley had never seen a person concentrate so hard. As she worked

with her pencil and eraser, feelings blew across the girl's face like seasons: She was disappointed, then frustrated, and finally pleased.

Stanley was very, very curious: What did her drawing look like? Did it look like him?

After nearly an hour, the girl paused. She held the book at arm's length, judging her work. Stanley's curiosity got the best of him, and he peeled his head forward to see.

The girl looked up, and he immediately snapped back into place.

Her big blue eyes narrowed. She took a step forward, studying him more closely than ever.

Stanley didn't dare move. The *Mona Lisa* was smiling as if she knew what a fool he'd been.

Then the strict teacher's voice barked something, and the girl snapped to attention. She fumbled to put away her pencil and sketchbook.

A guard by the door made an announcement, and people started exiting the gallery. The museum was closing!

The girl crept close to Stanley's painting. *"Au revoir,"* she whispered, and rushed out after her classmates. As she did, her sketchbook, which she'd shoved into a pocket of her satchel, fell out and onto the floor.

Stanley almost called out after her, but he caught himself. Soon the gallery was empty.

When he was sure the coast was clear, Stanley slipped from his frame and dropped to the floor. Creeping over to the girl's sketchbook, he picked it up, opened it, and found page after page of sketches—one painting after another, drawn in fine detail. There was even one of the *Mona Lisa*. Finally Stanley came to the girl's latest sketch.

Stanley was impressed. It looked just like him, except with a beard and a floppy hat. The girl with big blue eyes was very, *very* talented.

He turned back to the front cover. It read:

Le livre du
Etoile Dubois

L'école d'Art
22 rue d'Excaver
Montmartre, Paris

Her name is Etoile, Stanley realized. I have to return this to her!

Stanley looked up at the *Mona Lisa*. No one had tried to steal her . . . yet. She was safe for the night. Surely it would be okay for Stanley to stretch his legs after hanging on the wall all day—as long as he stayed in disguise and was back at his aunt's in time for dinner?

Stanley crept through the museum, moving silently along the walls and floors. He slipped behind one guard, and then another. He passed paintings by artists with names like Degas and Caravaggio. Stanley slithered down a staircase. He passed the pale bust of a woman whose arms had broken off; a sign said she was called *Venus de Milo*.

Finally Stanley found his way back to the front of the museum. The last of the visitors were leaving, and he caught a glimpse of a girl in a school uniform and a dark ponytail walking out the front doors—Etoile!

Stanley slipped into the coatroom. In a corner he found a large cardboard box labeled *Perdus et Trouvés*. Inside was a jumble of items, including clothing, umbrellas, and hats. This must be the lost and found, Stanley realized. He rummaged through the box and found a trench coat, a scarf, a dark hat, gloves, and tall boots. The coat and the boots were a little big, but Stanley felt that his shape was

well hidden. He found a box of tissues and took off his beard and makeup. Then he put Etoile's sketchbook in the coat's pocket.

He walked out of the coatroom, across the lobby, and into the sunshine.

Etoile was nowhere to be seen. Stanley found himself staring out at a river, which ran like a giant stone-lined canal through the center of the city. If he looked to his left, he saw a grand cathedral in the distance. He glanced right and saw the Eiffel Tower far away on the opposite bank. He looked down at the sketchbook. *Montmartre, Paris.* But which way was Montmartre?

As Stanley started walking, a sweet odor wafted through the air. At a nearby street cart, a jolly man in a cap was making razor-thin pancakes on a round griddle, topping them with fruit or chocolate. The smell hypnotized Stanley. His stomach grumbled, and he realized he hadn't eaten anything since breakfast.

"Une crêpe?" the man offered.

Stanley suddenly remembered Chef Lillou, the famous French chef who had plotted to steal La Abuela's secret ingredient in Mexico. In a fit of rage, he'd called Stanley a "crêpe." For the first time, Stanley understood why: A crêpe was even flatter than he was!

Stanley pulled out the pockets of his

overcoat to show that he had no money. The man shrugged, slathered a crêpe in fresh strawberries and cream, folded it up, and handed it to Stanley.

"Merci!" said Stanley gratefully. Then he held up Etoile's book and pointed to the address on the cover. *"S'il vous plaît?"* he said.

"Ah, Montmartre!" the man said. He pointed in the distance and made the shape of a tent with his fingers: a hill, that way.

Stanley said *merci* again and hurried on his way.

A Fresh Canvas

Winding his way through the streets of Paris, Stanley finally found a grand stone building in a maze of cobblestoned streets. The sign above the doorway read *L'école d'Art*, the same words that were on the sketchbook.

Stanley pushed open the giant door. Once inside he realized what *l'école d'art* meant: It was an art school. He

L'école d'Art

crept down a dimly lit hallway lined with empty classrooms until he came to one at the end, where he spotted the spidery teacher from the museum through the door's window. Inside, a handful of students were painting.

Stanley scanned the room. . . . There was Etoile, painting near the back! He'd found her! Now all he needed to do was find a way to return her sketchbook.

Stanley quickly removed his scarf,

hat, boots, and gloves. The less he wore, the more invisible he could make himself when he snuck inside. He even pulled off the puffy-sleeved shirt from the painting, so he was wearing only a white undershirt and his pants. He folded everything into a neat pile and hid it behind a trash bin in the corner of the hall.

Then, holding nothing but Etoile's sketchbook, he slipped beneath the closed door.

Stanley stayed low, skirting the edge of the room until he was directly behind Etoile. She was painting a young woman bending over a piece of lace she was mending. It reminded Stanley of one of the paintings he'd seen at the Louvre.

When the teacher's back was turned, Stanley popped up between Etoile and her painting. Her big blue eyes widened in surprise, but she stayed quiet. Then her eyes darted across the room—she was clearly worried that Stanley would get caught. As the teacher looked their way, Stanley quickly handed Etoile her sketchbook and folded his head and arms back behind her easel so his white T-shirt looked like a blank canvas itself.

Etoile immediately started painting on him. Stanley tried not to giggle as

she gently dabbed her brush against his chest.

Fifteen minutes later Stanley held his breath as the teacher came to look at Etoile's painting.

"*Très bien,* Etoile," the teacher said in an unusually soft voice. Stanley remembered that meant "very good."

Soon class was dismissed. Etoile said something to her teacher in French as the other students filed out—Stanley guessed that she was saying she wanted to finish her painting. The teacher left, closing the door behind her. And then they were alone.

Etoile said something excitedly in French.

Stanley rose up and shook his head. "I don't understand a word you're saying," he told her.

She grinned and poked his shoulder. "You were in the painting at the Louvre!" she said in English.

Stanley gulped. His mission was supposed to be a secret! "How do *you* know?"

The girl gestured at Stanley's T-shirt. He looked down and saw that she had perfectly re-created his painting.

"Who *are* you?" she said, her blue eyes dancing.

"My name is Stanley," he replied.

"I knew it!" she said, throwing up her hands. "I told my friend Martine you looked like Stanley Lambchop, the famous flat boy!"

Stanley felt himself blushing: Etoile knew who he was! "You dropped your book," he said. "I thought you would want it. You're a really good artist, you know."

Now it was the girl's turn to blush. "Madame Sévère would have been very angry if I had lost it. Thank you for returning it to me." Then she said, "What are you doing in a painting in Paris, anyway?"

"Uh, j-j-j-just visiting," Stanley stammered. He couldn't let on that he was a spy!

Etoile raised an eyebrow in disbelief. "Well," she said, "at least let me give you a tour of Paris. As a way of saying *merci*."

6

Beautiful City

"This neighborhood, Montmartre, has been home to great artists for centuries," Etoile told Stanley after he had put his puffy-sleeved shirt and trench coat back on and they returned to the street. "Claude Monet painted here. So did Pablo Picasso and Vincent van Gogh."

"Do you want to be an artist when

you grow up?" Stanley asked.

"I am an artist already," Etoile said. "L'école d'Art is a special boarding school for artists. Madame Sévère says the only way to paint like the masters is to copy them. Every day we go to a different museum to draw the paintings. And then we come back to our classroom and paint."

They walked down the hill of Montmartre, passing the famous Basilica of the Sacré-Coeur. As they wandered the streets of Paris, Etoile explained how the city was laid out in a series of rings, one inside the other. In the center was the neighborhood around the Louvre.

While they walked, Etoile asked

about Stanley's travels. He told her about performing with the Flying Chinese Wonders and jumping from a plane over Africa. He asked her questions about herself. *Etoile* meant "star." She had grown up in a seaside town in the south of France. Sometimes she missed her family. Stanley knew just how she felt.

Etoile and Stanley browsed the bookstalls on the Left Bank of the river Seine. In honor of his travels, Etoile bought Stanley an English copy of *Around the World in Eighty Days* by Jules Verne, one of France's greatest writers.

Then they visited the grand cathedral

Notre Dame, which Stanley had seen in the distance when he'd first exited the Louvre. It had gargoyles peering down from two huge towers and a colorful, round stained-glass window that stretched thirty feet across. The cathedral was nearly eight hundred years old!

Finally Etoile took him to the Eiffel

Tower. They rode an elevator to the top and looked out over the city.

Stanley had never been anyplace that was so full of art and beauty. "How do you say 'beautiful' in French?" he whispered.

Etoile looked at him with her big blue eyes. *"Belle,"* she whispered.

"Belle," Stanley repeated softly.

Suddenly Stanley was startled by a shout. *"Arrête!"* a familiar voice called. "Stop right there!"

From the elevator behind them leaped Agent Lunette. "I've been all over the city looking for you!" He put a firm hand on Stanley's shoulder. "You are late for dinner!" he said in Stanley's ear. "Let's go."

Stanley's heart lurched. He was about

to protest, but Agent Lunette stopped him with a stern look.

Stanley forced himself to say, *"Au revoir,* Etoile."

"B-but Stanley—" Etoile sputtered.

"Please don't tell anyone you saw me," he said sadly. "I'm sorry."

Etoile's blue eyes stared back helplessly as Agent Lunette dragged him away.

Minutes later Agent Lunette and Stanley arrived at Aunt Simone's apartment. She shrieked when she opened the door.

"Stanley!" she cried, wrapping her arms around him. She examined his face. "Did they hurt you?"

"Who?" Stanley wondered.

"The thieves who kidnapped you!" Aunt Simone said.

Agent Lunette grimaced and cleared his throat. "Monsieur Lambchop was not kidnapped, Mademoiselle."

"I went for a walk," Stanley said. "I made a friend."

"A friend!" Agent Lunette huffed. "Monsieur Lambchop, nobody was supposed to know you are here. You have put the mission in danger! We found you only because we alerted the entire police force, and an officer at la Tour Eiffel recognized you!"

"You're right, Agent Lunette," Stanley

said. "I made a mistake. And I'm sorry I worried you, Aunt Simone."

Agent Lunette straightened his glasses. "Is there anyone else in Paris who knows you have come, Monsieur Lambchop?"

Stanley shook his head. "No. And I don't think Etoile will tell anyone."

"Let us hope not," Agent Lunette said. "Because tomorrow you must guard the *Mona Lisa* once more."

False Appearances

The next morning, after he dressed and his aunt reapplied his beard and makeup, Stanley hung alone in his painting. The *Mona Lisa* looked over at him with her sly smile, as if she knew all about yesterday.

Stanley still felt terrible. He had disappointed Agent Lunette and scared his aunt. And when he thought of Etoile, his stomach ached. She had looked so confused and hurt when he had been taken away. She had been friendly and generous, and now he'd probably never see her again.

Museumgoers came and went, remarking on Stanley and his painting. The *Mona Lisa* smiled her smile.

Suddenly there was a loud clattering, and all the visitors in the gallery turned to look. Even Stanley shifted his eyes.

But it was just someone whose camera had dropped by accident.

The murmur of the crowd resumed, and Stanley brought his gaze back to the *Mona Lisa*. But it took all his control not to furrow his brow. Something wasn't quite right. He'd never noticed the tree beside her head. And had she always turned her body at him that way? She looked back at Stanley with her—

Wait a minute, thought Stanley. She's not smiling!

The *Mona Lisa* had been switched with a frowning fake!

Stanley scanned the crowd for anyone suspicious but saw nothing out of the ordinary. Then he looked up.

There was a masked person, dressed all in black, sticking to the ceiling of the gallery. The person had suction cups on both hands and legs . . . and over their back was slung the *Mona Lisa*! The burglar was creeping ever so slowly toward the door.

"Stop!" Stanley yelled, reaching out of his painting to point to the ceiling. "Thief!"

The thief began scrambling more quickly. Agent Lunette burst into the

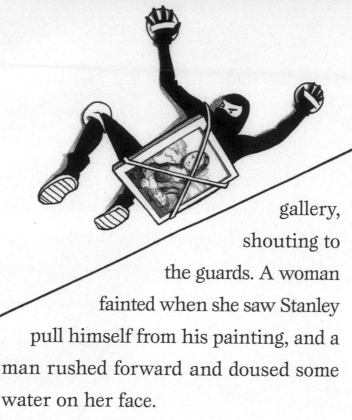

gallery,
shouting to
the guards. A woman
fainted when she saw Stanley
pull himself from his painting, and a
man rushed forward and doused some
water on her face.

"S'il vous plaît?" Stanley asked the
man, pointing to the water.

"This is no time for a water break!"
Agent Lunette shouted.

Without answering, Stanley splashed
some water on his face and hands.

Then he took three giant steps back, got a running start, and leaped onto the smooth gallery wall. His damp skin stuck like plastic decals on a window, just like when he had climbed the Washington Monument in Washington, DC.

By peeling his hands off and re-sticking them a few inches ahead of him, he was able to creep up the wall and onto the ceiling. The thief stuck and unstuck the suction cups speedily to flee.

Stanley inch-wormed across the ceiling as the crowd watched below. When he had almost caught up, the thief looked back, unstuck their right leg, and brought their knee down hard on Stanley's hand.

"Argh!" Stanley cried out in pain. The thief lifted their leg again, and Stanley grabbed the suction cup and hung on to it with one hand as he dangled over the crowd. Everyone gasped.

The thief jerked around, trying to shake Stanley loose. But Stanley wouldn't let go. Instead he grabbed the thief's leg with his other hand and started swinging back and forth, stretching the thief's leg farther and

farther. The thief groaned.
With a pop, the suction cup on
the other leg came unstuck
from the ceiling.

The thief was now
attached to the ceiling
by nothing more
than the suction cups
on their hands, with
Stanley swinging
from the thief's
legs like an
acrobat.

"Say *au revoir*," Stanley growled. He swung harder. With a squeak, the remaining two suction cups came undone.

"Nooooo!" cried the thief as they began to fall. Stanley swung up toward the ceiling as the thief fell down. He hooked his feet around the thief's shoulders. In midair, Stanley's body ballooned upward like a parachute, holding the thief beneath him.

They landed gently, with the *Mona Lisa* unharmed.

"You are under arrest!" Agent Lunette immediately cut the *Mona Lisa* from the thief's back and handed the painting to one of the officers. Then he pulled the thief's hands behind them and handcuffed them. Finally he pulled off the mask . . . and a short crop of dark hair spilled out.

Stanley sucked in a breath. "It's M-Madame Sévère!" he stammered. "She's a teacher at L'école d'Art!"

"As I tell my pupils," Madame Sévère said coldly, "the only way to paint like the masters . . . is to steal from them. My plan was perfect."

"No," Stanley replied. "Your plan fell *flat*."

All the museum visitors burst into applause as the officer led Madame Sévère away. Agent Lunette slapped Stanley on the back. "You have done it, Monsieur Lambchop! How can we ever repay you?"

Stanley thought for a moment. "There is one thing I'd like to do before I leave Paris."

Crêpe Stanley

Aunt Simone chose the restaurant for dinner: She said it was one of the finest in Paris. She wore a red dress to match her red lips and hair, and Agent Lunette was dressed in his best uniform, with medals pinned to his chest. Stanley had on a white shirt and a tie. When Etoile arrived, her dark hair was pulled back off her face. Her blue eyes sparkled in the candlelight.

While Aunt Simone and Agent Lunette talked to each other in French, Stanley leaned toward Etoile.

"Sorry I left you at the Eiffel Tower," he told her.

"I *knew* you weren't just visiting," Etoile said with a smile.

"Are you upset about your teacher?" asked Stanley.

Etoile's face darkened. "Madame made us copy masterpieces so she could have something to hang on the walls after she stole the originals. From now on, I will create my own masterpieces. Maybe one day they will hang in the Louvre."

"I hung in the Louvre for two whole days," said Stanley. "It's not as glamorous as it looks."

Etoile laughed.

Their meal was served, and Stanley remembered what his aunt had said when he first arrived: "This is France. Everything is delicious." He couldn't agree more. The beef Bourguignonne was rich and full-bodied, just like the province of Burgundy where Aunt Simone said it was a specialty. They agreed that the Camembert cheese tasted like the fields in the town of Camembert. There was cassoulet stew from Toulouse filled with beans and meat that made Stanley feel as if he were by a fireplace in a country castle.

"This is the finest meal I have ever had," Agent Lunette said. He looked into Aunt Simone's eyes. "And it is only partly because of the food."

Aunt Simone waved him away, but Stanley noticed her blushing. "Oh, Pierre, you are such a romantic!"

Stanley smiled. Just then the waiter appeared with the chef. "Monsieur Lambchop," he said, "the chef has something special for you."

Stanley looked up and nearly fell out of his chair. "No!" he cried. In his panic, he leaped up onto the table, grabbed a fork, and brandished it in front of him.

"Stanley, what's wrong?" cried Aunt Simone.

"The chef!" Stanley declared. "He's the one who chased me across Mexico, trying to steal La Abuela's secret!"

Chef Lillou held out his palms and
shook his head. *"Non! Non! S'il vous
plaît,"* he pleaded. "Please. I am not

the man I was. I was wrong. I want to apologize."

"You— What?" Stanley said, surprised.

"I have dreamed of seeing you again. I am glad you stopped me in Mexico. There was a missing ingredient in my life. I thought it was La Abuela's secret, but I was a fool. It was only when I came back to Paris that I found what was missing. It was *amour*—love. Everything changed when I found my true love. *I* changed."

Suddenly the hostess of the restaurant, a plump woman with a warm smile, appeared and wrapped her arms around the chef.

"*L'amour* changes everything," she said.

Stanley didn't know what to say. Meanwhile, Agent Lunette and Aunt Simone were staring dreamily into each other's eyes.

"*Oui*," Aunt Simone said lightly. "*L'amour* changes everything."

"*Oui*," Agent Lunette agreed. He took her hands and held them to his cheek.

Etoile wrinkled her nose at Stanley. "Maybe you should get down off the table now," she whispered.

Stanley thought that was a good idea, so he did.

The waiter wheeled over a silver platter. "I have created a new dish,"

Chef Lillou announced. "All over the world, Crêpe Suzette is known as one of the great French desserts. But I have made something new. Something *magnifique*. It is called Crêpe Stanley!"

The waiter lifted the silver dome off the platter with a flourish, and everyone oohed and ahhed.

Stanley and Etoile were finally full after they'd each eaten eight entire Crêpe Stanleys.

"My compliments to the chef!" Stanley told Chef Lillou, shaking his hand. "Can I take some home for my brother, Arthur, too?"

Au Revoir

Etoile and Stanley stood together beneath the Arc de Triomphe, a giant monument shaped like an arch in the center of the city. The lights of Paris twinkled around them.

"I feel so small standing here," said Etoile.

"I feel flat," said Stanley, "like usual."

Etoile laughed. "Will you write

me?" she asked.

Stanley nodded. Then he said, "Maybe one day I can come visit by airmail."

"I hope so," said Etoile.

Neither of them said anything for a long time.

"It's time for me to go," Stanley said at last. "*Au revoir*, Etoile."

"*Au revoir*, Stanley."

She turned to walk away—and then she spun around and gave Stanley a hug and a kiss on the cheek. And in that moment, the evening breeze almost blew him away.

One afternoon, several weeks later, Stanley and his brother, Arthur, were

lying on their beds in their room, daydreaming of Paris.

Arthur groaned. "I would give anything to have one more Crêpe Stanley. I can't believe I ate all forty-six of them the night you got home."

"Why don't you write Aunt Simone?" Stanley said. "I bet she could get Chef Lillou to send you some more."

"Why don't you just climb in an envelope and go get me some more?" replied Arthur.

"Why don't I flatten you with a bulletin board and then *you* can climb into an envelope?" teased Stanley.

Stanley reached under his pillow,

and pulled out the latest letter from Etoile. He never got tired of rereading her letters.

One of her paintings had been accepted into a special exhibition of young artists' work. It was a portrait of him called *La Terre Est Plate*: "The World Is Flat." He glanced up at his wall. Next to his bulletin board, he'd hung the T-shirt he was wearing the day they'd met—the one that she had painted on. He thought it was a masterpiece. He tucked the letter back under his pillow.

Arthur suddenly jumped from his bed and onto Stanley's. "I know how we can make more," said Arthur with a devilish grin, towering over Stanley.

"Arthur, don't—" Stanley said.

"*S'il vous plaît*," Arthur said. "May I please have . . ."

"Arthur!" Stanley giggled.

Arthur leaped in the air and threw himself down on Stanley, rolling over his body like a rolling pin.

"Crêpe Stanley!" he shouted.

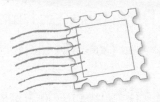

WHAT YOU NEED TO KNOW
ABOUT PARIS

The Eiffel Tower was built for the 1889 Paris World's Fair. It was the entrance arch for the fair.

The Louvre Museum was built in 1190 as a fortress. It was rebuilt as a royal palace in the sixteenth century and became a museum in 1793.

France is the most visited country in the world, with over 80 million visitors per year.

The largest bell in the Notre Dame Cathedral weighs about 26,000 pounds!

The *Mona Lisa* was stolen from the Louvre in 1911. After two years, French authorities finally found the Italian thief and recovered the painting.

It took almost 200 years to finish building the Notre Dame Cathedral.

A replica of the Statue of Liberty stands on Île aux Cygnes, a man-made island in the middle of the Seine River, which runs through Paris.

France makes almost 400 different types of cheese!

The Tour de France started in 1903 and is the most famous bike race in the world. Competitors bike almost 2,000 miles all around France over twenty-three days.

Montmartre, a hill in the northern part of Paris, is the highest point in the city.

Precious Creatures
A to Z

by: Kallen, Stuart A.

DATE DUE

Precious Creatures
A to Z

Kallen, Stuart A

DATE DUE	BORROWER'S NAME	ROOM NUMBER
MAY 1 2 1994	Jacqueline	2
JAN 1 3 1995	Amanda	2
FEB 3 1995	Ben	2

MORGAN HILL UNIFIED SCHOOL DISTRICT
15600 Concord Circle
Morgan Hill, California 95037-5451

MACHADO ELEMENTARY SCHOOL
MORGAN HILL UNIFIED SCHOOL DISTRICT
P. O. Box 927
Morgan Hill, Calif. 95037

GAYLORD

RECIOUS REATURES

 to Z

Written by Stuart A. Kallen

Published by Abdo & Daughters, 6535 Cecilia Circle, Edina, Minnesota 55439.

Library bound edition distributed by Rockbottom Books, Pentagon Tower, P.O. Box 36036, Minneapolis, Minnesota 55435.

Edited by Julie Berg

Photo Credits: Peter Arnold.

Kallen, Stuart A., 1955-
      Precious Creatures A-Z / written by Stuart A. Kallen; [edited by Julie Berg].
         p.   cm. - - (Target Earth)
      Includes bibliographical references (p. 63).
      Summary: Describes the origins and habitat of various animals on the verge of extinction, from the giant anteater to the zebra, and discusses attempts to preserve them.
      ISBN 1-56239-202-6
         1. Endangered species - - Juvenile literature.   2. Animals - - Juvenile literature.   [1. Rare animals - - Encyclopedias.   2. Wildlife conservation - - Encyclopedias.]   I. Berg, Julie. II. Title.
III. Series.
QL83.K35   1993   93-19060
591.52'9- -dc20   CIP
                        AC

The Target Earth Earthmobile Scientific Advisory Board

On the cover: Boy with parrots, courtesy of The Stock Market. Though parrots are not endangered, they—like all animals—are precious creatures.

Table of Contents

The grasslands of America were once filled with millions of bison.

All Creatures Great and Small

Once upon a time, the grasslands of America were filled with millions of wild bison. The skies were clouded with endless flocks of passenger pigeons. The seas were dotted with waves of whales. It seemed that they would be part of the American ecosystem forever. No one alive at the time could imagine a world without them. Then one day they were gone. Hunters had killed almost all of them.

Today, bison and whales are making a slow, steady comeback. They might never return in their former numbers. But with the help of humans, their numbers are steadily growing. Thanks to the work of a few caring people, we can go to Yellowstone National Park and see wild bison. And treaties have been signed by most countries to protect whales. Passenger pigeons, unfortunately, are now extinct.

Humans all over the world are learning from their past mistakes. Today, many people realize that every animal species is special. When air and water are polluted and forests are cut down, it affects more than humans. The water, air, and forests are home to thousands of species of animals, from microscopic bugs to the gigantic whales.

This book is about animals living on the edge. They are surviving in today's modern world. But they are barely hanging on in the wild. Their homes are being polluted, cut down, trampled by cattle, bulldozed, and permanently changed by the growing human population. Some of these animals are living in zoos. But they are disappearing in their wild and natural homes.

There is time left to save these animals. With our knowledge of the past and our dreams for the future, we can make this Earth a home for all of nature's creatures, great and small.

NTEATER

The giant anteater has no teeth. But that doesn't stop this toothless wonder from eating well. The giant anteater is nine feet long (2.79 meters) from snout to tail. Add another two feet (60.9 centimeters) for its long, sticky tongue, and you have eleven feet (3.4 meters) of insect-eating mammal. The anteater's tongue is as skinny as a worm, but that's perfect for digging deep into termite and ant nests. Their tongue is so sticky that the bugs stick to it like flypaper.

The giant anteater walks on its knuckles. This protects its huge nails. The nails need to be sharp so the anteater can rip open termite nests with a single jab. Anteaters are a hungry bunch. They eat over 30,000 ants and termites every day. At night, anteaters spread their huge, bushy tail over themselves like a blanket. Female anteaters carry their babies on their backs.

Anteaters live in the open grasslands of Central and South America. The growing human population is wiping out the anteater's natural habitat. There are no laws protecting anteaters, and they are on the verge of extinction.

An anteater lifting its nose to smell for enemies.

**B**EARS

Bears come in many shapes and sizes. The Japanese sun bear weighs 150 pounds (67.9 kilograms) and is only four feet (1.24 meters) tall. The Kodiak bear of Alaska is nine feet (2.8 meters) tall and weighs over 1,000 pounds (453 kilograms). In between there are brown bears, black bears, grizzly bears, and polar bears.

Bears love to eat fish. Brown bears stand in rushing mountain streams and catch salmon with their long, sharp claws. Polar bears float on icebergs in Arctic waters looking down in the clear cold waters for fish. Sometimes polar bears catch an unlucky seal. When they're not looking for their dinner in the water, bears eat nuts, berries, and roots.

Bears spend the winter in caves or holes under the snow. While the cold winds of winter howl outside their dens, female bears have babies. Then, for seven long months, the bears hibernate. Their breathing and heartbeat slow down. If you saw them hibernating you might think they were dead. But watch out! A mother bear with her cubs is a dangerous animal. Bears only attack humans when threatened. Unfortunately, humans still kill bears for sport or out of fear.

The wild areas where bears live are disappearing. A good example of this problem is the state of California. There were once so many grizzly bears there that bears became the state symbol. The California state flag has a picture of a grizzly bear on it. But the wilderness where they roamed for centuries was replaced with railroads, highways, grazing lands, and cities. The last grizzly bear was seen in California in 1922.

In Montana, Idaho, Alaska, and Canada, many of the forests and mountains where bears once roamed have been logged and mined.

Attitudes are changing. While some still hunt bears, many people respect the bear as the beautiful, wild creature that it is. In Yellowstone and Glacier National Parks bears still climb the crags and fish the streams as they have for thousands of years. Environmentalists are trying to stop the logging and mining in wilderness areas. Bears are making a comeback, but their existence hangs in the balance.

A grizzly bear in Glacier National Park, Montana.

**C**ONDOR

WHAT: BIRD

WHERE: UNITED STATES, SOUTH AMERICA

The Andean condor of South America is one of the most graceful birds in the world. It flies at speeds of up to eighty miles per hour (128 k/hr), with a wingspan of ten feet (3 meters). Its easy to see why the condor was worshipped by South American natives for hundreds of years.

The California condor may be seen gliding on the wind for hours, suspended in the air as if it were on a string. Condors have swept the skies of California since sabre-toothed tigers roamed the Earth. In those days, condors lived by the Pacific Ocean, from Mexico to the state of Washington.

As explorers pushed their way through the Americas, the condors retreated deeper and deeper into the wilderness. Today, there may be only fifty California condors left in the rocky canyons of Santa Barbara and Ventura counties.

Female condors do not lay eggs until they are six years old. Then, the bird only lays one egg every two years. For this reason, it is very hard for the birds to increase their number.

In the past, condors were killed for their feathers, which sold for up to one dollar apiece. Today, people are trying to pull the condor back from extinction. In the Los Padres National Forest, there is a condor sanctuary, where the birds may live in peace.

10

Condors have flown the skies of California since
sabre-toothed tigers roamed the Earth.

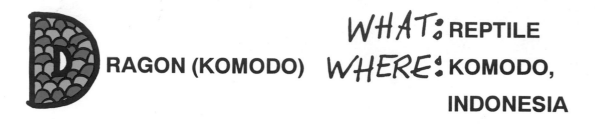

DRAGON (KOMODO)

If you thought that dragons only lived in cartoons, fairy tales and scary dreams, think again. On the tiny Southeast Asian island of Komodo, real live dragons lurk in the bushes. These giant reptiles certainly are a nightmare for whatever they catch.

The Komodo dragon is a giant lizard that grows up to ten feet long (3 meters) and can weigh as much as 365 pounds (164 kilograms). The island of Komodo where the dragons live is just a tiny piece of land 12 miles (19 kilometers) wide and 22 miles (35 kilometers) long. For centuries, stories of this monster lizard were considered to be fantasy tales of excited fisherman.

In 1912, scientists braved the rough waves and powerful currents that keep most people away from Komodo Island. The scientists wanted to see the dragon for themselves. After baiting a trap with a dead goat, the scientists captured a Komodo dragon. They discovered that the huge creature was identical to the eight-inch long (20.3-centimeter) monitor lizard.

Like the monitor lizard, the Komodo dragons are meat eaters. And they have big appetites. Komodos wait in ambush to pounce on whatever unlucky creatures walk by. They eat wild pigs, deer, and anything else they can catch. Komodos have been known to eat humans, but they have very bad eyesight. Humans usually see them first and stay out of the Komodo's way.

Komodo dragons are not threatened by hunting or human invasion. But there are only 7,000 of them in the world. A hurricane or volcano could wipe out the entire population.

There are only 7,000 Komodo dragons left in the world.

LEPHANT

Thousands of years ago, woolly mammoths and giant mastodons wandered over much of the Earth. Today those animals are extinct, but elephants, their nearest relatives, still live in Asia and Africa.

Elephants are the largest creature to walk the Earth. They can be ten feet tall (3.1 meters) and weigh over 10,000 pounds (4,530 kilograms). They're herbivores, which means they eat only plants. And they can eat up to 400 pounds (181.2 kilograms) of them a day. They wash it all down with 18 gallons (68.1 liters) of water. Elephants are remarkably intelligent. They have been trained by humans to perform tricks, and they are used as work animals in many Asian and African countries. With the strength of two dozen men, elephants are nature's bulldozers.

The elephant's life in the wild is ruled by a tightly-knit family system. Baby elephants stay with their mothers for eight years. They're pampered and tended around the clock. Mother elephants share child-rearing among themselves. If a mother elephant is off foraging for food, other elephants will watch her children.

Since elephants need so much food, they have to wander far and wide to find it. This brings them in contact with humans, who sometimes shoot the animals out of fear. Like many other wild animals, the areas of land where elephants roam are quickly being settled by growing human populations.

Elephants have been killed for years for their ivory tusks, which are used for jewelry and piano keys. Although it is now against the law, over 10,000 elephants are still killed every year for this purpose. Without immediate protection, elephants in the wild might disappear within the next ten years.

Mother elephants help each other raise their young.

**ROG**

There is more to frogs than the tiny green critters hopping through our yards and parks. The Pine Barrens tree frog found only in New Jersey and North Carolina is smaller than your thumb but croaks as loud as a duck quacks. The amazing Panamanian golden frog is spotted black and yellow. They look like hopping frog-tigers and they live only in a three-square-mile area of the Panamanian jungle.

Frogs and toads are usually land dwellers. But tadpoles—baby frogs that are hatched from eggs—are born with gills, like fish. Tadpoles live underwater until they grow old enough to change into frogs. This makes them amphibians, creatures who live both in water and on land.

We may think there are plenty of frogs "ribbeting" the night away. But certain types of frogs, like the Panamanian golden frog, are captured and sold as pets because of their unusual color. Other frogs are sold for use in laboratories. Frogs like the Pine Barrens tree frog are losing their wetland homes to bulldozers, housing developments, and shopping malls. Toads like the Sonoran green toad are having their numbers reduced by collectors.

So when you see a frog or toad hopping across your path, let it pass. They're probably on their way to eat some pesky bugs, like mosquitos, that want to bite you.

A Panamanian red-eyed tree frog.

ORILLA

WHAT: MAMMAL
WHERE: AFRICA

When watching gorillas in the animal parks, it's hard to believe that such large, powerful creatures could be threatened with extinction. But looks are deceiving. Although gorillas stand over six feet tall (1.8 meters) and weigh up to 400 pounds (181.2 kilograms), they are usually gentle, shy creatures. They live on a diet of plants, which they shove into their mouths with both hands. When people come near them in the wild, they usually sneak away.

Scientists have revealed that gorillas are very smart animals. The legendary gorilla "Koko" has been trained to use over 500 sign language words. Koko uses sign language to tell jokes, curse, invent words, and even lie when it suits her.

Wild gorillas live in Africa. It is estimated that 5,000 to 15,000 live in the jungles along the equator. Gorillas also live on the slopes of extinct volcanoes. Their numbers are dwindling daily. Although killing gorillas is against the law in Africa, their meat is considered a gourmet treat. Their body parts are also used for the religious rituals of some African tribesmen.

In the wild, gorillas live peaceful lives; eating, sleeping, and raising their young. They live in groups of twenty, led by an older male, called a silverback, whose back is covered with silver-gray hair. Young gorillas are about the size of human children, and they love to swing on vines, wrestle, and tumble on the ground. Like some human children, they whine when they want something and throw temper tantrums when they can't get their way.

Gorillas push through the dense jungle foliage all day long. If a gorilla sees some tasty leaves at the top of a tree, they scamper to the top to eat them. Even a 400-pound (181.2-kilogram) silverback can easily scale a tree. At night, gorillas make a bed of leaves, pull a bush over themselves for a blanket, or find a handy tree to lounge in.

If someone bothers a gorilla, it might get very mad. It will chatter, throw branches in the air, and charge full-speed-ahead. Usually the gorilla will stop just short of jumping on a person. Most sensible people run away by that point. If not, the gorilla might hit a person and give them a nasty bite.

If gorillas feel comfortable with a group of humans, the gorillas might let the humans sit and watch them for hours. Gorilla-watching has become a big tourist attraction in Africa. The interest of outsiders might save gorillas who face extinction from human hunters. In addition, Africa's growing human population is rapidly cutting down the gorilla's jungle home.

A mountain gorilla of Rwanda, Africa.

 IPPOPOTAMUS

The word hippopotamus (hip-o-POT-uh-mus) comes from the Greek words that mean "river horse." But hippos are more closely related to elephants than horses. In fact, next to elephants, hippos are the second largest land animals in the world. An adult hippo stands about 5 feet (1.5 meters) tall and is almost 14 feet (4.3 meters) long. They're hard to get on a scale, but hippos have been measured to weigh between 3,000 and 8,000 pounds (1,364 to 3,636 kilograms).

Hippos live in the wild, south of the Sahara Desert in Africa. They spend most of their days in or near water to escape the hot African sun. They gather in groups of five to fifty animals. Heavy hippos don't float in water, but simply walk along the bottom of shallow lakes, lagoons, and rivers. Their eyes, ears, and nostrils stick up just above the surface of the water. This way the hippo can see, hear, and breathe while remaining hidden under the water.

The pygmy hippo, which is about the size of a pig, is a miniature hippopotamus. Pygmy hippos live in the jungles of West Africa. They are shy creatures and are rarely seen by humans.

The wetlands of Africa face pressure from the growing human population. Hippos, like thousands of other creatures, depend on these wetlands for their survival. Coupled with the value of their ivory tusks to illegal hunters, the hippo faces double trouble. Most hippos in the wild today live on game preserves and parks where they are protected. But poachers and other people are threatening the world of the hippopotamus.

Hippos depend on wetlands for their survival.

**BEX**

Judging from the ancient paintings on the walls of caves in Spain and France, the ibex was a common sight long before civilization reached Europe. The handsome ibex with their long, sweeping horns, have been drawn on caves with loving detail.

The ibex, cousin to the mountain goat, once lived in the high Pyrenees Mountains of Spain and France. They were also found in the Alps of Italy, France, Austria, and Switzerland. There, they lived above the tree line, only coming down from their rocky perches during the harshest winters. In the summer, the ibex grazed on the sweet grasses in alpine meadows.

The long horns of the ibex were thought to possess magical powers and the ibex were hunted to near-extinction. By 1700 the ibex had become a rare sight in the Pyrenees. By the twentieth century, the population had been reduced to less than twenty animals.

In the Alps, the ibex had been killed off by 1850, except for about sixty animals. King Victor Emmanuel gave this group protection in 1865, putting them on the royal hunting preserve, the Grand Paradiso. The preserve became the Grand Paradiso National Park in 1922. By 1933, the ibex had increased their number to 6,000. World War II caused much starvation and hardship, and the ibex were hunted and eaten by hungry refugees.

Today, under the protection of the European governments, the ibex population is bounding back in both the Alps and the Pyrenees.

The ibex, cousin to the mountain goat,
was hunted to near-extinction.

JAGUAR

The largest cats in the Americas are jaguars (JAG-wars). They can be six to nine feet (1.8 to 2.8 meters) long, including their tail, and weigh from 120 to 300 pounds (54.3 to 135.9 kilograms). Jaguars are fearsome hunters who will attack alligators, monkeys, deer, turtles, and frogs—anything for a meal. Jaguars will even use their long claws to scoop fish out of the river. The jags lure the fish to one spot by swishing their tail as bait.

Jaguars roam over huge tracts of land, up to two hundred square miles (518 square kilometers). They're loners, and usually travel and live alone in the wilds. Female jaguars give birth to one to four cubs. The babies stay with their mother for over a year until they find their own territories.

Years ago, thousands of jaguars roamed all Southwestern, South, and Central America. Today, most live in the rainforests where they can hide from hunters. As the rainforests are chopped down, the jaguars are losing the wilderness in which they hunt and live.

In years past, a jaguar coat was considered a status symbol by the rich and famous. Today, through education, many people are avoiding coats made from endangered species like the jag. Their survival depends on the survival of the rainforest and their protection from hunters. Farmers and ranchers also kill jaguars because the cats kill livestock.

Jaguars are part of a family of large cats. Almost all of these animals are threatened with extinction for the same reasons as the jaguar. They include the fastest land animal on Earth, the cheetah, of Africa and Asia, who can run up to sixty miles per hour (96.5 k/hr). Other large cats such as the cougar of the United States, the snow leopard of Asia, the leopard and lion of Africa, the Siberian tiger of Russia, and the tiger of South Asia are being hunted and hounded out of existence. Without the help of caring humans, they may soon disappear altogether.

Jaguars are the largest cats in the Americas.

OALA

With its soft, silvery fur, shiny black nose, and teddy-bear shape, the koala (koe-AH-la) is a favorite animal of people all over the world. This was not always the case. At one time, this lovable Australian marsupial was hunted almost to extinction. The soft beautiful fur that make the koala so lovable also made it very attractive to trappers and coat makers.

Koalas are often called bears, but bears they're not. Koalas are marsupials—animals who carry their young in a pouch. Koalas are less than one inch (2.54 centimeters) long at birth. They crawl into their mother's pouch and stay there for six months. Then the baby koala crawls onto its mother's back and clings there for several more months. At age four the koala is full-grown, and about three feet (one meter) long. Koalas live about twenty years.

Australia is home to over three hundred types of eucalyptus trees. The koala is a very picky eater and eats only a very few kinds of eucalyptus leaves. In addition, the leaves have to be at a certain state of growth. This makes it difficult for the koala to find the more than two pounds (one kilo) of leaves it must eat every day. The koala lives in eucalyptus trees and has special pouches in its cheeks where it can store leaves for later eating.

At the beginning of the twentieth century, millions of koalas were killed every year for their fur. More than two million koala skins were exported from Australia in 1920. This trend continued for decades. By 1939, the koala had all but disappeared from Australia's forests.

After World War II, strict laws protecting the koala were enacted. Since that time, preserves have been set aside where koalas may live unharmed. In some places the animals are doing so well that there are too many of them. These animals are removed to more rural forest preserves. Today, after years of savage hunting and terrible massacre, the lovable koalas are making a comeback in the land "down under."

Koalas are often called bears, but are really marsupials.

Madagascar is an island the size of Texas off the southeastern African coast. The island broke off from the African continent over sixty million years ago. Because of this, the wildlife on the island evolved without outside interference. This makes Madagascan wildlife some of the most unique in the world.

One of the island's uncommon animals is the lemur (LEE-mer), a cousin of the monkey. At one time, forty kinds of lemurs shared Madagascar with giant tortoises, chameleons, and 500-pound (225-kilogram) birds whose eggs were as big as soccer balls. That was before thousands of people moved to Madagascar to clear the forests for farmland. Since that time, dozens of Madagascar's animals have become extinct, including many types of lemurs. Today there are twenty kinds of lemurs.

Lemurs come in all shapes and sizes, from the tiny mouse lemur to the monkey-size avahis and sifaka. Unfortunately, the huge, gorilla-sized lemur is extinct. Lemurs have large, round copper-colored eyes that give them a haunted look. They live on a diet of leaves, bark, flowers, fruits, and young plant shoots. Lemurs spend their days in trees, climbing, jumping and running from branch to branch.

All lemurs are noisy. Sifaka lemurs get their name from the Malagasy word see-fah, which means hiccup. The animals let out long, loud hiccups after a good meal.

Since humans first settled on Madagascar, over ninety percent of its forests have been chopped down. As much as seventy percent of the island's plants and animals have been driven into extinction. But the people of Madagascar love the lemurs. They have set aside a dozen areas where all of Madagascar's animals will be protected. Scientists are experimenting with removing lemurs from Madagascar to other islands where there are less people. But the hunger and needs of the human population of Madagascar must be met before the lemurs and their wild friends will be safe in their home territory.

Lemurs come in all shapes and sizes. This is a monkey-sized sifaka lemur.

ANATEE

Hu-manity is a word used to describe the human population. Huge manatee (MAN-uh-tee) are words used to describe giant marine mammals that Chistopher Columbus once thought were mermaids. Today, no one would mistake the twelve foot (3.7 meter) long, 3,500 pound (1,587 kilogram) manatee for a singing mermaid. But when Columbus first spotted the giant potato-shaped creatures floating lazily in the water he wrote that "mermaids were not quite as lovely as he had been led to believe." Of course, Columbus thought he was sailing to China not North America. But because of this mistake, manatees, and their cousins dugongs, are known as "sirenia." Sirens are mythical mermaids mentioned in the ancient Greek legend *The Odyssey*. Many people associate the manatee with other sea mammals like walruses, whales, dolphins and seals. But the manatee's closest relative is the elephant.

The Florida manatee is a well-known creature that lives in the warm Atlantic waters off the coast of Florida. In the summer they may be seen as far north as Virginia and as far west as Louisiana. If it weren't for human beings, their barges, and power boats, manatees would have an easy life. They just love to bob and float in warm tropical waters. There, they eat up to 200 pounds (90.3 kilograms) of sea grasses every day.

Manatees are described as very affectionate. They love to touch and rub against each other. When humans dive into waters where manatees live, the animals will nuzzle the diver's faces with their rubbery lips. They even gently grasp an arm or leg and pull the divers close into what can only be called a hug. Unfortunately, this affection can work against the manatee. They have been seen nuzzling boat propellers, their biggest enemy.

The official manatee population of Florida was about 1,200 animals in 1990. This puts the manatee on the list as the most endangered marine mammal. The manatee is protected by several state and federal laws that prohibit killing, injuring, or harassing the animal.

Another problem is that manatees are slow to reproduce. A female can only have one baby every two years. With the small number left alive, manatees cannot reproduce fast enough for their numbers to stay even.

Manatees are described as very affectionate animals.

 **N**UMBAT

The numbat (NUM-bat) has a long skinny tongue like that of an anteater. And like the anteater, the numbat's specialized diet consists of ants and termites. As a matter of fact, numbats eat over 20,000 termites a day! But unlike the anteater, the numbat is a small marsupial that lives in Australia.

Numbats are pretty little animals that look like rust-colored, striped squirrels. They run through Australian forests at a hyper pace looking for rotting logs which contain termite nests. Once they find such a log, they uncurl their tongue, which is half as long as their body, and suck up the squirming meal. A female numbat performs this task with her babies, usually four of them, hanging onto her back.

Numbats often fall prey to land-clearing projects and brush fires. When Europeans first came to Australia in the early 1800s they brought dogs and cats with them. They also brought foxes and rabbits to hunt. Numbats were easy victims for the dogs, cats, and foxes from another land. Today numbats survive on wildlife reserves where they are protected from outside predators and human hunters.

The numbat eats over 20,000 termites a day.

 **CELOT**

While much is known about the large regal cats like lions and tigers, little attention is paid to the lesser cats like ocelots (AH-sel-ot). But many smaller cats have been hunted to near-extinction. At least ten of the thirty-five species of small cats are endangered.

The ocelot is native to the southwestern United States. At one time, ocelots roamed through Louisiana and Arkansas, but these creatures were wiped out by hunters years ago. The ocelot lives in its greatest numbers in the dense forests of Central and South America.

Ocelots, like all other members of the cat family, are excellent hunters. Their sleek muscular bodies can run down almost any prey. The sharp teeth and claws of the ocelot make short work of any animal they catch. If it weren't for humans and the desire for their beautiful coats, ocelots would have few natural enemies.

The selling of ocelot furs was outlawed in most places years ago. However, a coat made of ocelot skins can be bought on the black market for up to $100,000. With prices like these, its not hard to see why hunters are tempted to trap ocelots. Coupled with the destruction of their natural habitat, the rare and beautiful ocelot may soon disappear.

Other small cats that are threatened are the bobcat, the lynx, the serval, the clouded leopard, the pampas cat, and the mountain lion.

Ocelots, like all members of the cat family,
are excellent hunters.

ANDA

Pandas were first mentioned by Chinese writers 4,000 years ago. But until quite recently, pandas remained a mystery to those who lived outside the remote mountain jungles of China, Nepal, and Tibet. Because of their secretive ways, and the rugged wilderness that is their home, much about the panda remains a mystery today.

Pandas live at mountain elevations of 5,000 to 14,000 feet (1,550 to 4,340 meters). The slopes of these mountains are covered with dense forests of pine, oak, and bamboo. The bamboo jungles of this region are so thick that humans can barely cross through them. Low, drifting clouds further fog the forests where the panda live.

Pandas can be up to six feet tall (1.8 meters) and weigh up to 350 pounds (160 kilos). Bamboo is the panda's main food source. The fact that the plant grows in this area is as unusual as the panda itself. Bamboo is a very fast growing plant. Some types of bamboo grow more than three feet (one meter) in one day. But bamboo grows mostly in hot, wet climates. The bamboo that grows in the snowy, cold high altitudes of China is an oddity. But without the bamboo there would be no panda.

In the spring and summer, pandas feast on the green and tender sprouts and leaves of the bamboo. Sometimes pandas will eat vines and irises. In the winter, bamboo dries up and sheds its leaves. During the winter season, pandas eat the rock-hard stems and branches of the plant. This gives the panda very strong teeth and jaws, not to mention a cast-iron stomach to digest the woody splinters.

The first live panda was captured by Ruth Harkness in 1936. It was very unusual at the time for a woman to cross China and capture animals in the harsh mountain wilderness. Harkness brought a two-week-old baby panda to the Chicago Zoological Society in Brookfield, Illinois. "Su-Lin" was the first live panda seen by most Westerners. Soon, young pandas were being carried out of the mountains at an alarming rate. Many died along the way and few lived very long in zoos. In the mid-1950s, China passed laws forbidding the capture of pandas. At last, these wild animals were protected.

Pandas were first mentioned by Chinese writers 4,000 years ago.

**Q**UETZAL

WHAT: **BIRD**

WHERE: **CENTRAL AMERICA**

Quetzals (KET-sahl) are striking scarlet and golden-green birds. Their beautiful tail feathers grow up to two feet (61 centimeters) long. These feathers were highly prized by the ancient Mayan and Aztec civilizations who lived in the Central American region. The quetzal was thought of as a sacred bird by these cultures. It was associated with the plumed serpent-god Quetzalcotl. Quetzal feathers were highly prized. They were woven into headdresses and ceremonial garb. Today, the quetzal is the national bird of Guatemala and decorates the money and the flag of that country. Quetzals are thought of as symbols of freedom, because they do not survive well in captivity.

Quetzals live in rainforests that grow on Central American mountainsides. They flutter from branch to branch and feed on fruit, insects, frogs, lizards, and snails. Females lay eggs, but the males sit on them until they hatch. Since the eggs are laid in holes in trees, the male bird must fold his long tail feathers over his head to sit on the eggs. The feathers stick out of the nesting hole. By the end of the nesting season, the feathers are broken and bent. But quetzals grow new feathers after every breeding season.

The quetzal's beauty is also driving it to extinction. Although it is illegal, poachers can earn a month's pay by selling live quetzals to zoos and bird collectors. In addition, farmers are chopping down the rainforests and destroying the quetzal's native environment. Unless the destruction of the Central American rainforest is stopped, the quetzal may soon disappear.

Quetzals live in rainforests that grow on
Central American mountainsides.

RHINOCEROS

WHAT: MAMMAL
WHERE: AFRICA, ASIA

Rhinoceros (rye-NAH-ser-us) have roamed the African continent for more than twenty million years. Today, with rhino horn selling for more than gold, poachers have all but wiped out this once mighty beast. Only thirty years ago, as many as 100,000 rhinos lived in Africa. Today their number may be as low as 2,500. At the current rate of poaching, rhinos may be extinct in a few years.

Rhinos are the distant cousins of the horse and the zebra. There are five species of rhino. The Indian and the Javan rhino have one horn. The Sumatran, the white, and the black rhino have two horns. People in China, Korea, and Taiwan believe rhino horns possess magical qualities. Powdered rhino horn has also been proven to reduce fever in sick people. Because of this, rhino horn sells for over $4,000 for 2.2 pounds (one kilo). This is twelve times the average yearly income of people who live around rhinos.

Compared to their ancient ancestors, modern rhinos are midgets. But next to the elephant and the hippopotamus, the rhino vies for top-billing as the largest land animal. And rhinos are built like tanks, with massive bodies, tree-trunk legs, short necks, and wide chests. The largest rhinos stand over six feet tall (1.8 meters) and weigh up to 4,000 pounds (1,818 kilos). The largest rhino horn ever found was 67 inches (170 centimeters) long.

In the wild, thick-skinned rhinos can crash through the sharpest thorns or withstand the attacks of the sharpest-clawed predators without a scratch. Rhinos are vegetarians and eat leaves, grass, and even cactus. They also need huge quantities of water to survive. Africa's hot, dry summers can kill many water-loving rhinos. During these times, rhinos will roll in mud to keep their skin moist.

Rhinos are nearsighted and some cannot tell the difference between a human and a tree standing only fifteen feet (4.65 meters) away. They do have a sharp sense of smell, however, and can smell attackers at a distance. When a rhino does recognize an enemy, such as a man, it will put its head down and charge. Rhinos have been clocked at speeds of up to 35 miles (56 kilometers) per hour. They've been known to tip over cars and trucks when startled.

Rhinoceros have roamed the African continent for more than twenty million years.

 **LOTH**

WHAT: MAMMAL
WHERE: SOUTH AMERICA

Sometimes a really slow person is called "slothful." But most humans are not quite as slow as sloths. Sloths usually travel at about seven feet (2.17 meters) per minute. They may take twelve hours to travel one mile (1.6 kilometers). Sloths are faster than snails, which can take thirty-two hours to travel one mile (1.6 kilometers). By comparison, humans walk at about three miles (4.8 kilometers) per hour. If sloths are in a hurry they may speed up to about fourteen feet (4.3 meters) in a minute.

Sloths live in the rainforests of South America. They usually hang out in trees where they move around at about two feet (60.9 centimeters) per minute. Some sleepy sloths spend their entire lives in one tree, idly eating the leaves and fruit that hang nearby. Sloths don't walk, so if they ever come out of the trees, they must pull themselves along the ground using their claws. Surprisingly, sloths are good swimmers and have been known to swim across wide lakes.

Not too surprisingly, sloths are also the sleepiest animal, spending 80 percent of their slothful lives snoozing. The saying goes, "A rolling stone gathers no moss," but sloths often have algae growing on their fur. This gives them a greenish appearance that helps hide them from predators.

Unfortunately for the slow-moving sloth, the fast-paced world is catching up to it. The sloth's rainforest home is getting chopped down at an alarming rate. If the rainforests are gone, the sleepy sloth will no longer survive.

Sloths live in the rainforests of South America.

TURTLE & TORTOISE

WHAT: REPTILE
WHERE: VARIOUS PLACES

Long ago, when European explorers traveled the oceans, they had a problem. How could they keep enough fresh food on board the ship to feed the sailors? The giant turtle or tortoise was the answer. (Turtles live mostly in water. Tortoises live mostly on land.) The sailors would catch hundreds of the 350-pound (158.5-kilogram) reptiles, and lash them to the decks of their ships. Then, they would kill them and eat them, one at a time, as they crossed the open ocean. In the eighteenth century, on Galapagos Island, off the coast of South America, Portuguese sailors captured 30,000 tortoises in eighteen months. The slow-moving land creatures were easy to catch. Today, giant tortoises are protected by law in many places.

Green sea turtles have faced the same problems as their land cousins. Today, in countries all over the world, giant sea turtles are still killed for their skin, shells, meat, and eggs.

But the sea turtle is a fascinating creature who needs protection to survive. The story of how they reproduce is an amazing one.

Green sea turtles lay eggs on tropical beaches all over the world. At sunset, one night a year, female turtles crawl from the sea up onto the beach. By the time it is dark, the beach may be dotted with over 1,000 of the giant reptiles. The turtles drag themselves above the high-tide line, and start digging. After the turtle digs a deep hole, big enough to hold her body, she lays up to 100 eggs in the wet sand. Then, just as slowly as she climbed the beach, she crawls back into the water and swims off into the dawn.

About two months later the eggs explode all at once. Thousands of baby turtles, as big as your hand, pop out of the sand. Immediately, they scramble for the water. This is a dangerous time for the turtles. Hundreds of hungry sea gulls, vultures, crabs, and other predators hover nearby. Humans too, wait with nets.

Some turtles live a long time — as much as one hundred years. Turtles that survive the ordeal of being born are tough and wily. Their strength and toughness have left the species unchanged for over 200 million years. Protecting turtles and tortoises is a hard job. Many types of turtles are endangered, including the radiated tortoise, the loggerhead turtle, the green turtle, and the 1,500-pound (679.5-kilogram) leatherback turtle.

The sea turtle is a fascinating creature that needs protection to survive.

NGULATES

Ungulates (UNG-je-lates) are hoofed mammals with either two or four toes. Some of the most well-known ungulates are domestic animals like cows, sheep, goats, and camels. But there are several species of wild ungulates that are on the brink of extinction.

Wild ungulates, like their domestic cousins, have provided humans with skins, wool, and food for centuries. Ungulates include such animals as gazelle, elk, deer, and mountain goats. Today, many of them fall prey to hunters' bullets. Some hunters kill ungulates for food, some for their skins, and some, only for their beautiful horns.

The dorcas gazelle that roam wild in the remote areas of northern Arabia, are hunted by "sportsmen" who shoot at them out of car windows with powerful rifles.

Swamp deer of India are easy to capture in open grasslands. Poachers sell the deer's horns to boat builders who use them for screws.

The majestic bighorn sheep of the western United States have long been shot as pests or trophies. When Europeans first crossed the Rocky Mountains, there were millions of the bighorns. Today, there are only a few scattered groups.

The gaur is the world's largest wild cattle. Also known as the seledang, gaur live in the forested mountains of southern Asia. Gaur have been nearly exterminated by diseases caught from domestic cattle.

The addax lives in the bleakest parts of the Sahara. But its splayed hoofs are not quick enough to outrun hunters on camels.

Ungulates include such animals as gazelle, elk, and bighorn sheep.

VICUÑA

WHAT: MAMMAL
WHERE: SOUTH AMERICA (PERU)

The vicuña (vi-KOON-yah) is lucky to wear a coat of the finest wool in the world. One of two wild species of the camel family, the vicuña needs its wool coat to keep warm in the cold air of the Andes Mountains.

Vicuñas live high in the Andes Mountains, at altitudes of 11,400–18,700 feet (3,475–5,700 meters). Against a backdrop of snow-capped peaks and rocky crags, these small graceful animals make a beautiful sight. Vicuñas stand about five feet (1.5 meters) tall, weigh from 77 to 143 pounds (35 to 65 kilograms) and can run at speeds of up to 30 miles (48 kilometers) per hour. They live in herds, with the largest male acting as the leader. When hunters want to kill vicuña, they shoot the leader first. Without a leader, the herd mills around in fright and confusion. Then they are easy pickings for the hunters.

In ancient times, no one but Inca kings were allowed to wear coats woven from vicuña wool. The Incas, who lived in the region before Europeans arrived, valued the vicuña. To obtain their wool, the Incas carefully herded the vicuña together in spring and sheared their coats. The vicuña grew new wool by wintertime and no harm was done. Today, the ancient tribesmen have been replaced by the modern poacher.

The poachers find it easier to kill the vicuña before shaving it. Although many countries have banned their import, suits made from vicuña wool may fetch up to $6,000.

Many vicuña today are running free in safety zones on refuges high in the Andes Mountains. The most famous of these is known as the Pampa Galeras, National Vicuña Reserve. They reproduce quickly, like deer, and their numbers are growing. If people stop wearing clothes made from vicuña wool, the animals may be saved. After all, no one needs a coat of vicuña wool as much as a vicuña does.

Vicuñas live high in the Andes Mountains at altitudes of 18,000 feet.

ALRUS

WHAT: MAMMAL
WHERE: ARCTIC OCEAN, ALASKA

When the Europeans first laid eyes on Canada's Gulf of St. Lawrence, they saw the largest concentration of walruses in the world. Called "sea oxen" or "sea cows" by the early explorers, it wasn't long before the walruses fell to hunters' guns. The Europeans wanted the walrus' blubber for soap and oil. They also wanted their 39 inch (one meter) long tusks for jewelry and piano keys. Men made incredible fortunes from walrus products. Within eighty years, hundreds-of-thousands of walruses were killed. By 1680, there were none left in the St. Lawrence. For the next three hundred years, the walrus would be tracked and slaughtered until the 1920s, when there were only 40,000 left on Earth—all of them in the frozen Arctic.

Male walruses grow to 13 feet (4 meters) in length. Females are somewhat smaller. Walruses can weigh up to 3,500 pounds (1,587 kilograms). Today they live in the open waters near the edge of polar ice where they feed on clams, starfish, and sea urchins. The huge animals eat 100 pounds (45 kilograms) of food every day. That's about 800 large clams!

Walruses use their long tusks for defense, to break through ice, and to pull themselves out of the water. Sometimes walruses will sleep on land's edge, using their tusks like ice picks to prop their heads up out of the water. Walruses have long bristly moustaches that filter food on muddy ocean bottoms.

Walruses swim north in the summer and south in the winter. They often hitch rides on ice floes on their migration. During breeding season, huge male walruses fight with each other over females. Their loud, shrieking bellows can be heard up to one mile (1.6 km) away. When baby walruses are born, they can swim immediately. But they nurse on their mothers for up to two years. Female walruses are loving mothers who watch their babies very carefully.

Walruses have been protected for more than twenty years and their numbers are increasing. Today there are almost 250,000 of the creatures living in the Arctic.

Walruses swim north in the summer and south in the winter.

XENICUS LYALLI OR STEPHEN ISLAND WREN
WHAT: BIRD
WHERE: NEW ZEALAND

Xenicus lyalli (ZEN-e-cus LY-al-ee) is the Latin name for the Stephen Island wren. The story behind the bird's extinction is a fascinating one. It is also a story that was repeated in many places when Europeans brought their house cats to foreign shores.

Stephen Island lies in Cook Straight between the North and South islands of New Zealand. The island is only one square mile (2.6 square kilometers) in area but rises 1,000 feet (305 meters) out of the ocean. The towering rock of Stephen Island was an ideal place to build a lighthouse. The project was completed in 1894.

Little known to the lighthouse builders, Stephen Island contained a remarkable wren. The bird could not fly, and is believed to have the smallest natural range of any bird. The flightless Stephen Island wren was a mottled yellow and brown and only four inches (10 centimeters) long.

Perhaps most remarkable, the wren was not discovered by humans. It was discovered by Tibbles, the lighthouse keeper's cat. When Tibbles brought home this rare wren (dead), the lighthouse keeper notified scientists. The scientists realized that the bird was unique and carefully preserved its body. Several specimens of the bird are preserved today in museums in New Zealand, New York, Pittsburgh, and Cambridge, Massachusetts.

Like flightless birds of many islands, the wren was no match for the cunning cat. Before long, Tibbles had wiped out the entire species of wrens on Stephen Island. Today, the rock wren (xenicus gilviventris) and the bush wren (xenicus longipes) are other members of the xenicus family that are threatened with extinction.

The rock wren and the bush wren are threatened with extinction.

YAK

WHAT: MAMMAL
WHERE: TIBET, WEST CHINA, INDIA

The yak has been used as a tamed domestic animal for centuries. The stout woolly beasts provide Tibetan mountain people with milk, food, and "yak power" to carry, pull, and haul. But these sure-footed animals are threatened in the wild. The six foot (1.8 meters) tall, ten foot (3.1 meters) long yak looks like a very furry cow. In fact, yaks will breed with cows.

Yaks in the wild have been killed for centuries. At one time they wandered over much of China, India, and Tibet. But centuries of hunting have pushed the animals to the highest, most remote parts of the Himalaya Mountains. But yaks have adapted to the harsh mountain conditions. Their long blue-black hair, which reaches almost to the ground, offers protection against bitter mountain winds. And their slow, steady stride lets them easily climb through the rocky terrain. Yaks are equipped with heavy curved horns that afford them protection against most enemies.

Yaks are endangered in the wild but laws have been passed to protect them.

*At one time yaks wandered over much of
China, India, and Tibet.*

ZEBRA

WHAT: MAMMAL

WHERE: EAST AFRICA, KENYA, ETHIOPIA

What animal could better show nature's diversity than the "striped horse" or zebra? Like their cousins, horses and donkeys, zebras travel in large packs and live on grass.

In Africa, thundering herds of the zebra roam far and wide in groups of up to 500. Their constant search for food and water takes them over the central, southern, and eastern plains of the continent. The large pack of zebras attracts many predators, including lions and wild dogs. These animals depend on zebras for their food, catching and eating the weak and the slow.

People have been fascinated with zebras for centuries. In the third century, a Roman emperor used zebras to pull his chariot. In Africa, people have always used the zebra for work animals and for food and hides.

There are three species of zebra. Grévy's zebra is the largest, standing about five feet (1.5 meters) tall and weighing between 780 and 950 pounds (354 to 432 kilograms). Like all zebras, its mouth contains large, chisel-shaped teeth that are perfect for grinding and chomping grass. When the mood strikes, the zebra will let out a bray like that of a donkey. Grévy's zebras live in the semi-arid regions of Somalia, Kenya, Ethiopia, and the Sudan.

There are two kinds of mountain zebra, both rare. The Cape mountain zebra and Hartmann's mountain zebra are both small, standing only four feet (1.2 meters) tall and weighing about 600 pounds (273 kilograms). Mountain zebras live in the stony hills of South Africa. Because of overhunting, mountain zebras are endangered. There are only several hundred mountain zebras left. They live in Cape Mountain Zebra National Park.

At one time, huge herds of zebras were a common sight in Africa. Today, many of the herds are gone. Drought, hunting, and the growing population threaten zebras. But parks and wildlife refuges have been put aside to protect this black animal with the white stripes. Or is it a white animal with black stripes? Whatever you decide, zebras, like all of nature's creatures, must be protected so that they will be here for future generations.

In Africa, herds of zebra roam far and
wide in groups of up to 500.

# NDANGERED ANIMALS: FACTS AND FIGURES

The animals covered in this book are just some of the more popular, well-know animals that are endangered. People naturally care much more about the lovable panda than they do about an endangered clam or crawfish. But all species are important and have a right to exist. Just to give you an idea of the scope of the problem, are some facts about endangered species listed below.

- Scientists guess between 5 and 30 million species of plants and animals live on Earth. No one knows for sure.

- Only 14 million species of plants and animals have been identified and given names.

- Only 4,000 of those species are mammals.

- There are 750,000 species of insects.

- Only 1 in 100 species are bigger than a bumble bee.

- 50 to 90 percent of all species on Earth live in tropical rainforests.

- The Earth loses 51 million acres of tropical rainforest every year because of logging.

- The Earth loses 3,800 acres of tropical rainforest to logging every hour.

- At current rates of cutting, all tropical rainforest will be gone in 177 years, or about three generations.

- One quarter of all the Earth's species of plants and animals will be gone by the year 2050 if current practices are not stopped.

- 50 to 150 species of plants and animals become extinct every day.

• 500 species of plants and animals have become extinct in North America since the Pilgrims landed on Plymouth Rock in 1620.

• The United States government lists 617 species as endangered as of 1992.

• Only 6 species have been removed from the endangered list since 1972 because they have recovered.

• 7 species have been removed because they have become extinct.

• 33 endangered animal species are growing in number.

• 122 endangered animal species are shrinking in number.

• At the current rate of decline, all animals on the U.S. Endangered Species list will be extinct in the next 50 years.

# ANIMAL PROTECTION ORGANIZATIONS

A complete list of all endangered mammals, birds, amphibians, and fish may be obtained from the United States Fish and Wildlife Service's Office of Endangered Species. Write for a free booklet:

Division of Endangered Species
U.S. Fish and Wildlife Service
452 Arlington Square
Washington, D.C. 20240

Other organizations:

The Nature Conservatory
1815 North Lynn Street
Arlington, VA 22209

Izaak Walton League of America
1400 Wilson Blvd.
Level B
Arlington, VA 22209

The National Wildlife Federation
1400 Sixteenth St. N.W.
Washington, D.C. 20036-2266

The National Audubon Society
950 Third Avenue
New York, NY 10022

The World Wildlife Fund
1250 24th Street N.W.
Washington, D.C. 20036

There are also dozens of organizations dedicated to saving specific animals. Lists can be found at your local library.

Write letters! Get involved! Save the animals now!

Glossary

Amphibians - Cold-blooded animals who live in water and on land. Frogs are amphibians.

Captivity - To be kept under the control of another. Humans keep certain animals in captivity.

Den - Shelters where animals live. Bears make their dens in caves.

Housing development - Areas where many new houses are built at one time. Some housing developments threaten natural areas where wildlife live.

Domestic animals - Animals that have been tamed by humans. Dogs, cats, horses, cows, and sheep are some domestic animals.

Ecosystem - A large region such as a forest, wetland, or sea and all the plants and animals that live there.

Endangered - A word to describe a species that is in danger of extinction.

Environmentalist - A person who studies and works to save the air, water, land, and animals from pollution and harm.

Exterminate - To totally destroy.

Extinct - A word used to describe animals and plants that have not been seen in the wild for more than fifty years.

Foliage - The leaves of a plant.

Foraging - Searching for food.

Habitat - A place where an animal or plant naturally lives.

Herbivore - Any animal that eats only plants. Elephants are herbivores.

Hibernate - To spend the winter asleep or inactive. Bears hibernate.

Larva - The immature, wingless form of an insect.

Mammal - A warm-blooded animal that feeds milk to its young. Mammals are usually covered with hair. Human beings are mammals.

Marsupial - A type of mammal that carries its young in a pouch on the outside of the mother's body. Koalas and kangaroos are marsupials.

Microscopic - Something so small it can only be seen with the aid of a microscope.

Poacher - A person who kills or traps animals illegally.

Population - The total number of human beings living in a place.

Predator - A type of animal that kills other animals for food. Tigers are one type of predators.

Primates - A group of mammals with very advanced brains. Primates have hands with thumbs for grasping things. Monkeys, gorillas, chimpanzees, and human beings are all primates.

Reptiles - A cold-blooded animal with scales and a backbone. Turtles, lizards, and snakes are reptiles.

Sanctuary - A place that provides protection from harm. Many animals are protected on wildlife sanctuaries.

Species - A group of related plants or animals.

Connect with Books

Arnold, Caroline. *Hippo*. New York: William Morrow & Company, 1989.

Arnold, Caroline. *Zebra*. New York: William Morrow & Company, 1987.

Cadieux, Charles, L. *Wildlife Extinction*. Washington, D.C.: Stone Wall Press, Inc., 1992.

Carwardine, Mark. *The Encyclopedia of World Wildlife*. Seacaucus, New Jersey: Cartwell Books, 1986.

Eberle, Irmengarde. *Pandas Live Here*. Garden City, New York: Doubleday & Company, Inc., 1973.

Guinness Publishers. *Remarkable Animals*. London: Guinness Superlatives, Inc. 1987.

Harper & Row. *Harper & Row's Complete Field Guide to North American Wildlife*. New York: Harper & Row, 1981.

Lavine, Sigmund A. *Wonders of Rhinos*. New York: Dodd, Mead & Company, 1982.

Laycock, George. *America's Endangered Wildlife*. New York: Grosset & Dunlap, Inc., 1969.

Marten, Michael, May. John and Taylor, Rosemary. *Weird & Wonderful Wildlife*. San Francisco: Chronicle Books, 1983.

McClung, Robert M. *Lost Wild World*. New York: William Morrow & Company, 1976.

Rand McNally. *Children's Atlas of World Wildlife*. New York: Rand McNally & Company, 1990.

Ranger Rick Books. *Endangered Animals*. National Wildlife Federation, 1989.

Reynolds, J. E. III and Odell, D.K. *Manatees and Dugongs*. New York: Facts on File, 1992.

Shuttlesworth, Dorothy E. *The Wildlife of Australia and New Zealand*. New York: Hastings House Publishers, 1967.

TARGET EARTH™ COMMITMENT

At Target, we're committed to the environment. We show this commitment not only through our own internal efforts but also through the programs we sponsor in the communities where we do business.

Our commitment to children and the environment began when we became the Founding International Sponsor for Kids for Saving Earth, a non-profit environmental organization for kids. We helped launch the program in 1989 and supported its growth to three-quarters of a million club members in just three years.

Our commitment to children's environmental education led to the development of an environmental curriculum called Target Earth™, aimed at getting kids involved in their education and in their world.

In addition, we worked with Abdo & Daughters Publishing to develop the Target Earth™ Earthmobile, an environmental science library on wheels that can be used in libraries, or rolled from classroom to classroom.

Target believes that the children are our future and the future of our planet. Through education, they will save the world!

TARGET®

Minneapolis-based Target Stores is an upscale discount department store chain of 517 stores in 33 states coast-to-coast, and is the largest division of Dayton Hudson Corporation, one of the nation's leading retailers.